D1252705

ABOUT THE AUTHOR

Aileen Fisher lives in a cabin on a ranch in the foothills of Colorado—a cabin that she helped build with her own hands. From the window at her desk she looks beyond fields and pine-covered hills to Arapahoe Peak.

Miss Fisher was born on the Upper Peninsula of Michigan. When she was five, her family moved to a farm near Iron River, and it was there that she learned to love the outdoors and to look forward to the changing seasons. Her first poetry was written for the high school column of the local newspaper. Since that time she has written many books and plays for children. She attended the University of Chicago and later received a degree in journalism from the University of Missouri.

ABOUT THE ILLUSTRATOR

Peter Parnall is especially well suited, by interest and by ability, for illustrating BUT OSTRICHES... His major interest is in "critters." In fact, he studied veterinary medicine while in college, and his hobbies are raising horses and breeding fighting chickens on his farm in New Jersey.

Mr. Parnall's fine illustrations for children's books have been on the *New York Times* Best Books lists in 1967 and 1968, and have been shown at the American Institute of Graphic Arts.

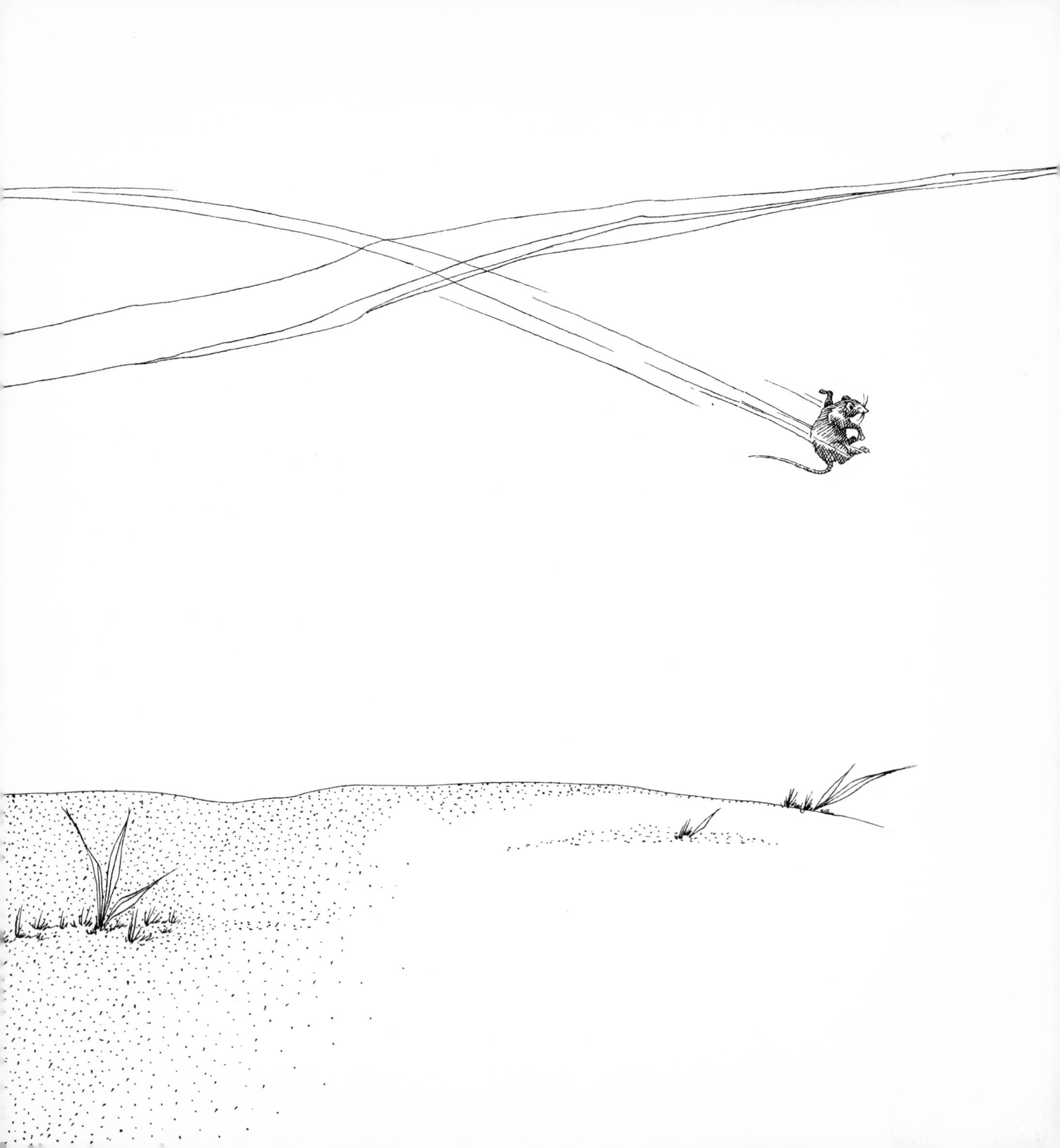

For an ostrich
is quick
with a hard,
fast kick
from his horny toe . . .
and away you go!
in a style not planned,
for, you understand,
a bird in the scrub
in ostrich-land
is better by far
than a bird in hand.

And as for a *pet* . . .

You'd better beware:

That gleam
in an ostrich's eye,
that glare
suggests you conduct yourself
with care
lest you suddenly sail
through the bright
blue air
and land with a Thump
in the sand somewhere.

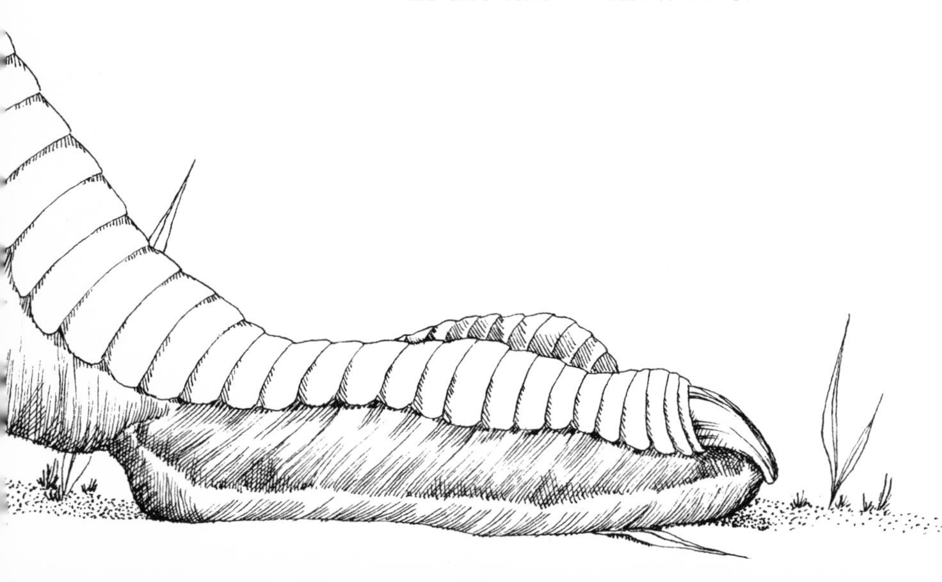

But OSTRICHES
never
are half so clever.

They go their way
with nothing to say
that even resembles
a mild "Good day."

Parrots
and mynah birds
and crows
often can speak
in people's prose:

They have a most
astonishing way
of imitating
the things we say.

They make amusing
and pleasant pets
and no one hearing them
soon forgets
their quick "Hi-ho,"
and "What do you know?"
and "Danger ahead,"
and ". . . told you so."

But OSTRICHES . . .
no one
has ever said
there's much of a tune
in that periscope head.
Canaries
are vastly preferred
instead.

Over a berry bush
and thistle
songbirds carol
and trill and whistle.

Out in the elm,
the oak, the apple,
birdsong mingles
with shadow-dapple.

Under the leaves
where sprinkles glitter
songbirds warble
and tweet and twitter.

Some have voices
that lilt and rise
to marvelous heights
for a bird that size.

Oh, a bird that sings
is a bird to prize!

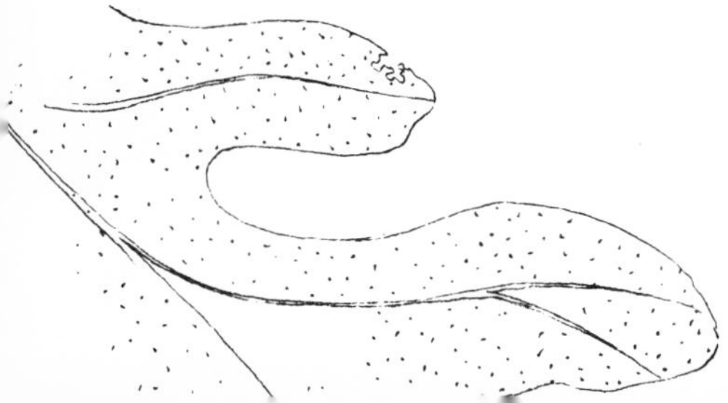

U.S. 1554632

No wonder the parents cooperate!

Most of the eggs
you're apt to see
in a nest in the grass,
a bush, a tree,
hatch in a couple of weeks,
or three,
when the scrawny chicks
in the shells break free.

But not for OSTRICHES.
No, sir-ee.

For them
the hatching
is far from quick.
The shell of an ostrich egg
is thick,
and *weeks* are needed,
as many as eight,
for ostriches' eggs
to incubate.

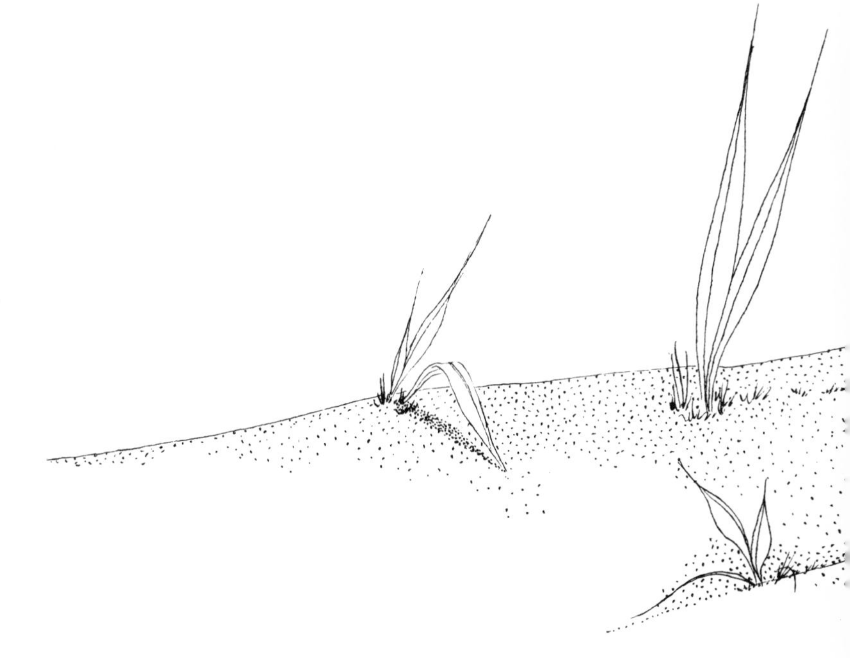

But OSTRICHES . . .

Maybe
you'll get a shock
to hear that sometimes
a showy cock
has several wives,
all plainly dressed,
who lay their eggs
in the selfsame nest.

And the sum of the eggs,
in case you've wondered,
may be numbered
at half a hundred,
with all the parents
cooperating
by taking turns
with the incubating.

One in a petrel's nest,
I've heard.

Two for a hummingbird,
and loon.

Three, four, five
in the month of June
for birds like sparrows
and jays and larks
with nests in the meadows
and woods and parks.

Six for a wren,
or even *seven,*

The nest of a grouse
may hold *eleven.*

More for a quail
and his bobwhite cousin:
eggs in their nests
may pass a *dozen.*

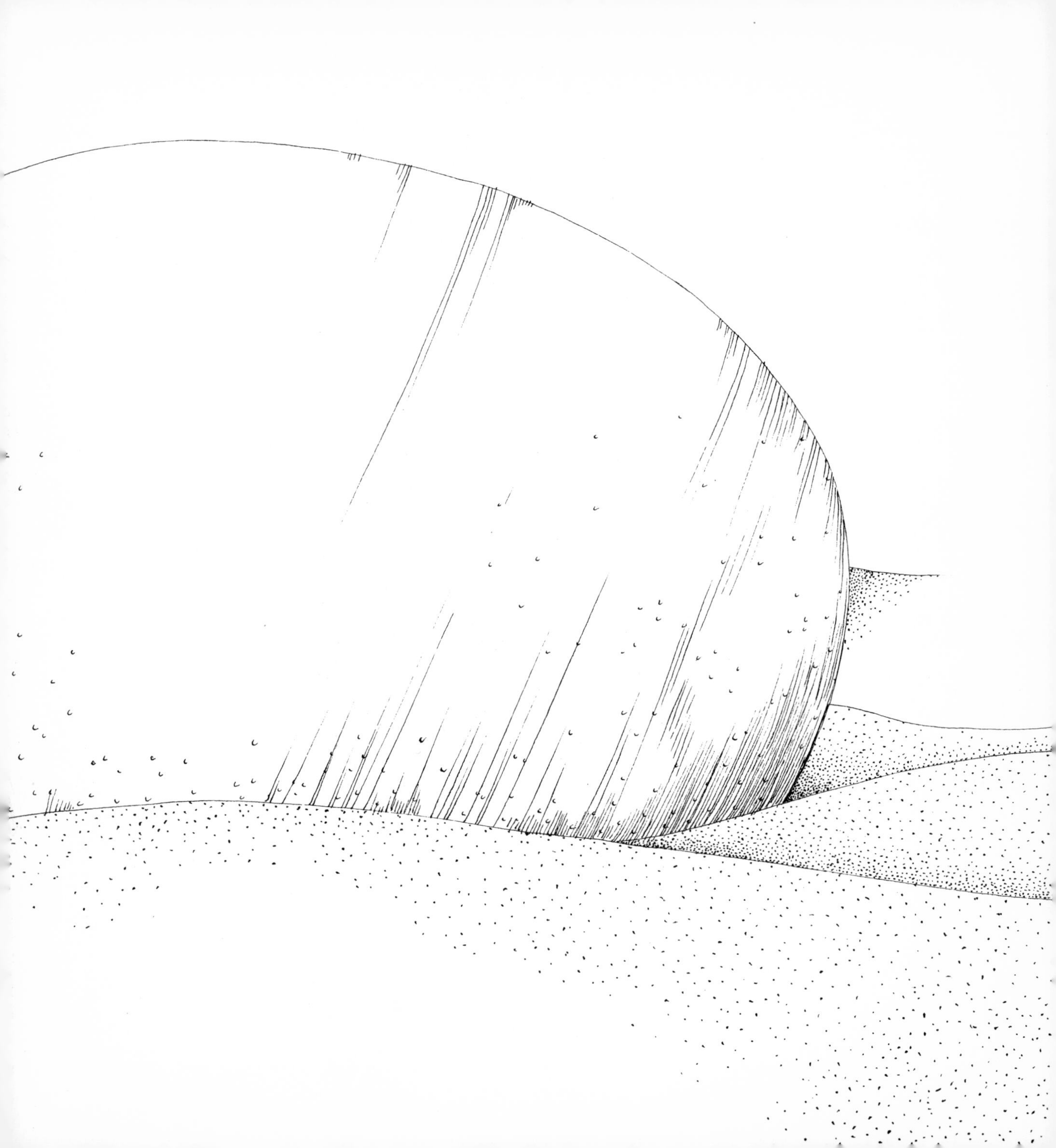

But OSTRICHES' eggs!

One heaps a plate.

Three pounds *apiece*
is the average weight.

So several people
may feast for days
on one of the eggs
that an ostrich lays
in the shallow nest
in the sun-warmed sand
in the open country
of ostrich-land.

As a general thing,
in a single word,
how many eggs
in the nest of a bird?

Cackle and strut!
The barnyard hen
boasts she has laid
an egg again.

She has to lay nine
or even ten
to make a supper
for gentlemen,

For each of the eggs
her clack announces
usually weighs
but two small ounces,
which means a nestful
of twenty-four
would weigh three pounds
or a trifle more
at a poultry shop
or the grocery store.

But OSTRICHES
never
use grass or fluff
or twigs or mud at all.
A scoop in the sand
is nest enough
for a bird so lighthouse tall,

A scoop in the sand
to hold the eggs
where Papa sits
on his cramped-up legs
night after night
in calm or storm,
keeping the eggs
both safe and warm,

A scoop in the sand
where through the day
an ostrich wife
whiles the time away
as the round eggs hatch
in the cream-white batch
in a nest the ostrich
has made "from scratch."

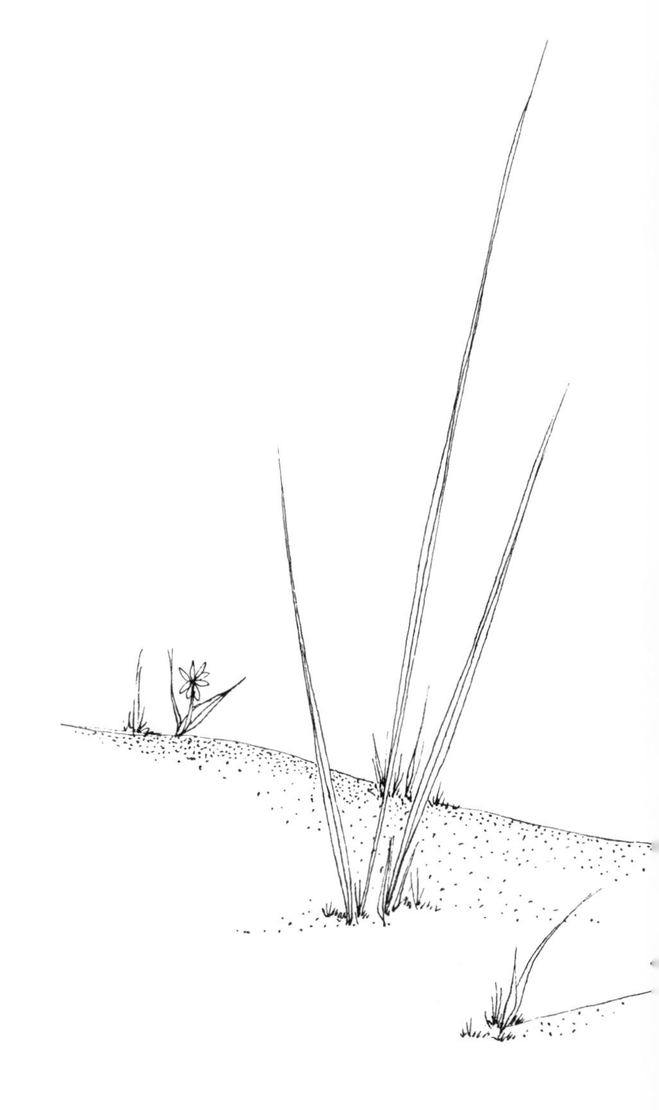

Nests of grass
under grassy shadows
please the birds
of the fields and meadows.

Sticks for some birds,
mud for others,
feathers and fluff
for fussy mothers . . .

A well-drilled hole
makes a nest for a flicker.
Woodpeckers probably
drill one quicker.

Birds of the woods
(not albatrosses)
fashion their nests
of leaves and mosses.

Birds of the marsh
and along its edges
weave in rushes
and grass and sedges.

Three hundred pounds
to contemplate!

But OSTRICHES grow
to be biggest of all
(some of them actually
eight feet tall),
with a watchtower neck
and a head as small
as a good-sized orange
or tennis ball,
and brains no more
than a walnut's size
back of their wary
gleaming eyes.

Oh, ostriches grow
to be very great
not only in size
when they stand up straight
but some reach
three hundred pounds
in weight . . .

And bigger than *that*
is a whooping crane,
and trumpeter swan
in its wild domain.

And bigger than that
the frigate birds grow
and sea gulls
and eagles
and buzzards
and herons
and hawks in the treetops
and owls in the barrens,

A hummingbird
is small as a minute.

A wren is larger
and so is a linnet,

And so is a robin,
a bluejay, a crow,

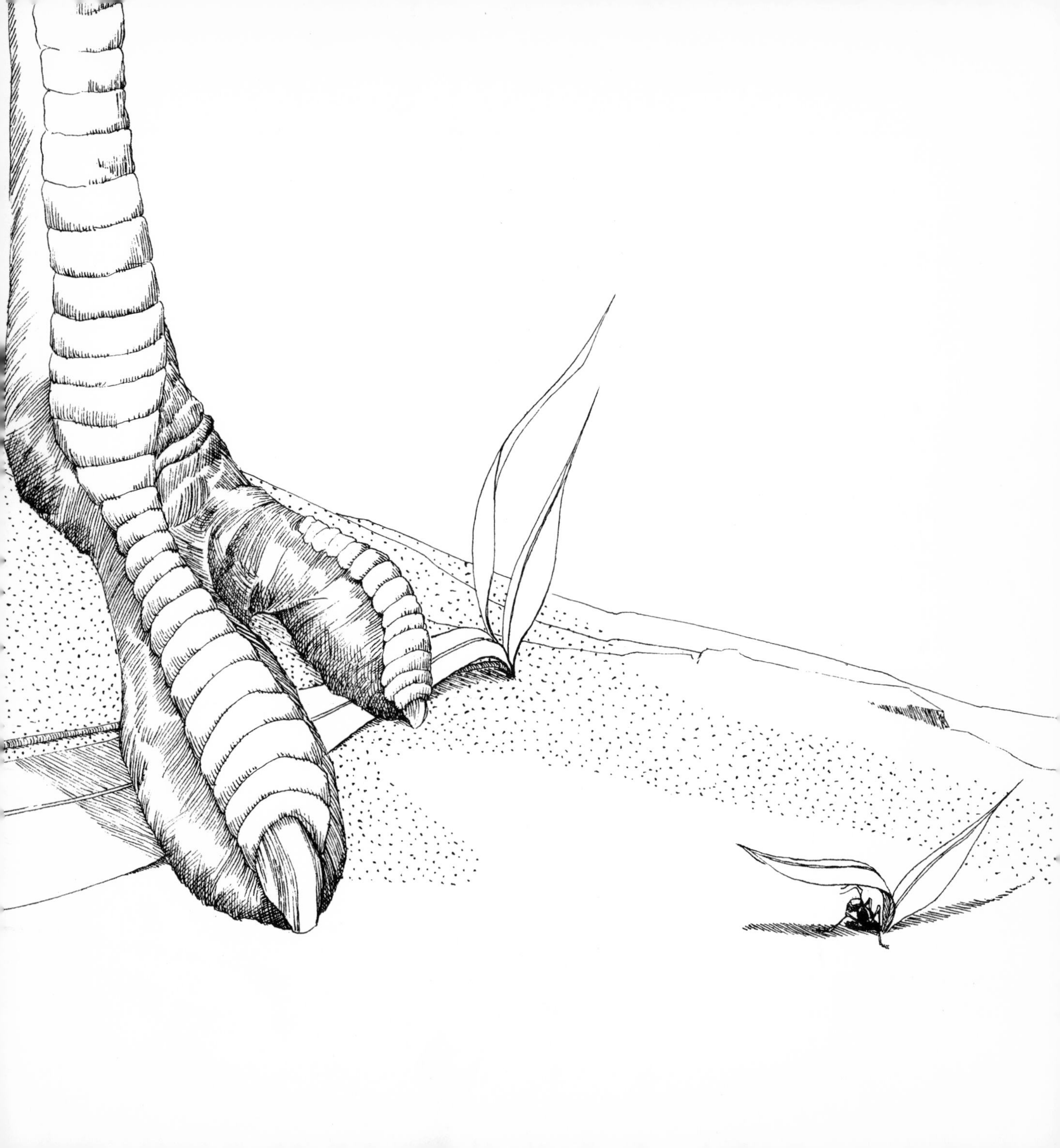

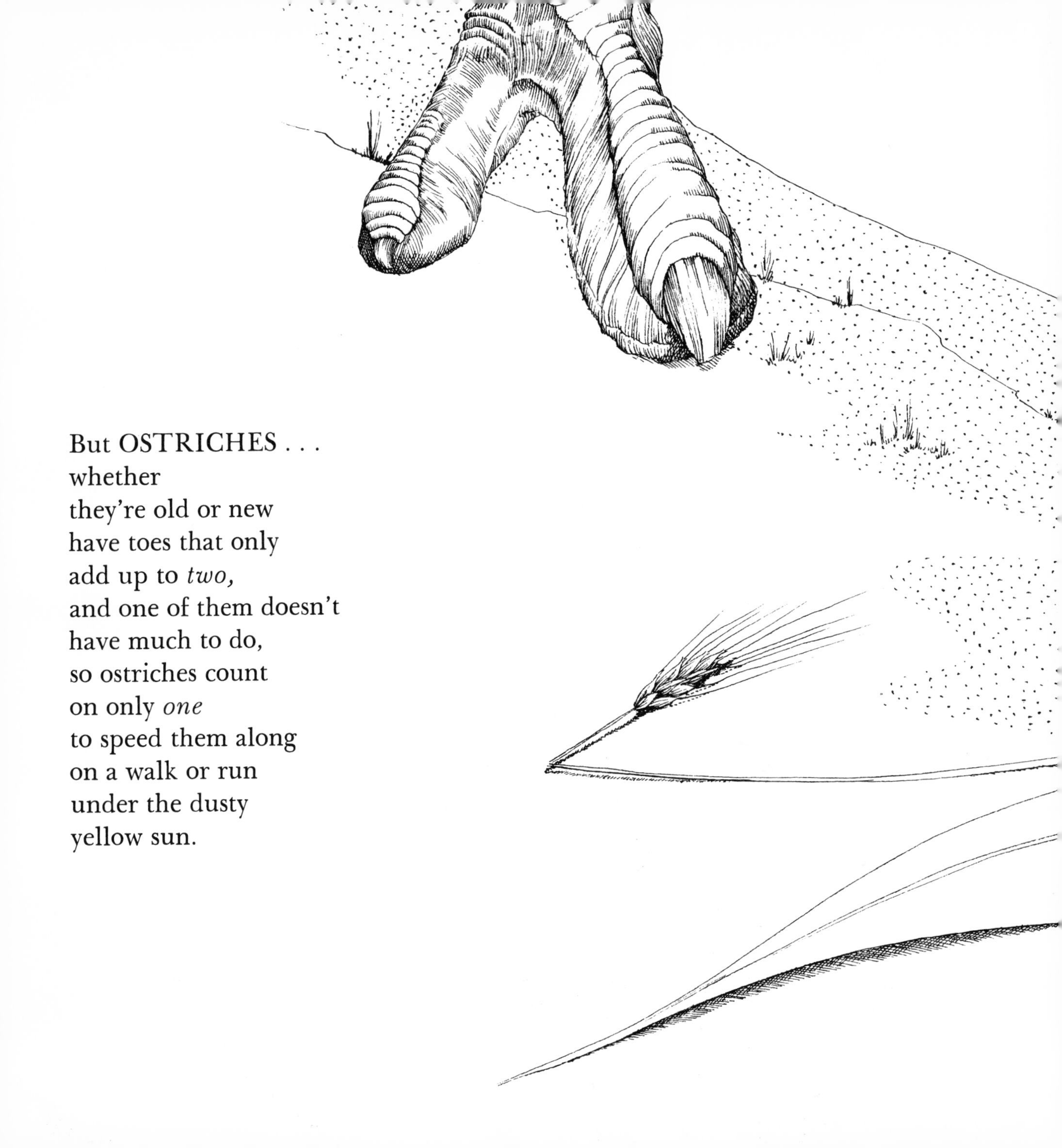

But OSTRICHES . . .
whether
they're old or new
have toes that only
add up to *two,*
and one of them doesn't
have much to do,
so ostriches count
on only *one*
to speed them along
on a walk or run
under the dusty
yellow sun.

Tall birds,
small birds,
nearly all birds
have four toes
that leave a track:

Long toes,
strong toes,
weak toes,
freak toes . . .
three in front
and one in back.

(And they *don't*,
by the way,
with danger at hand
go bury their heads
in the sunny sand.)

But OSTRICHES,
mind you,
are truly fleet
by using only
their horny feet
with pads underneath
to stand the heat
of the African sand
of ostrich-land.

Stepping high
with a mighty stride,
they gambol over
the countryside
at such a speed
that they could pace
a very fast horse
in a steeplechase.

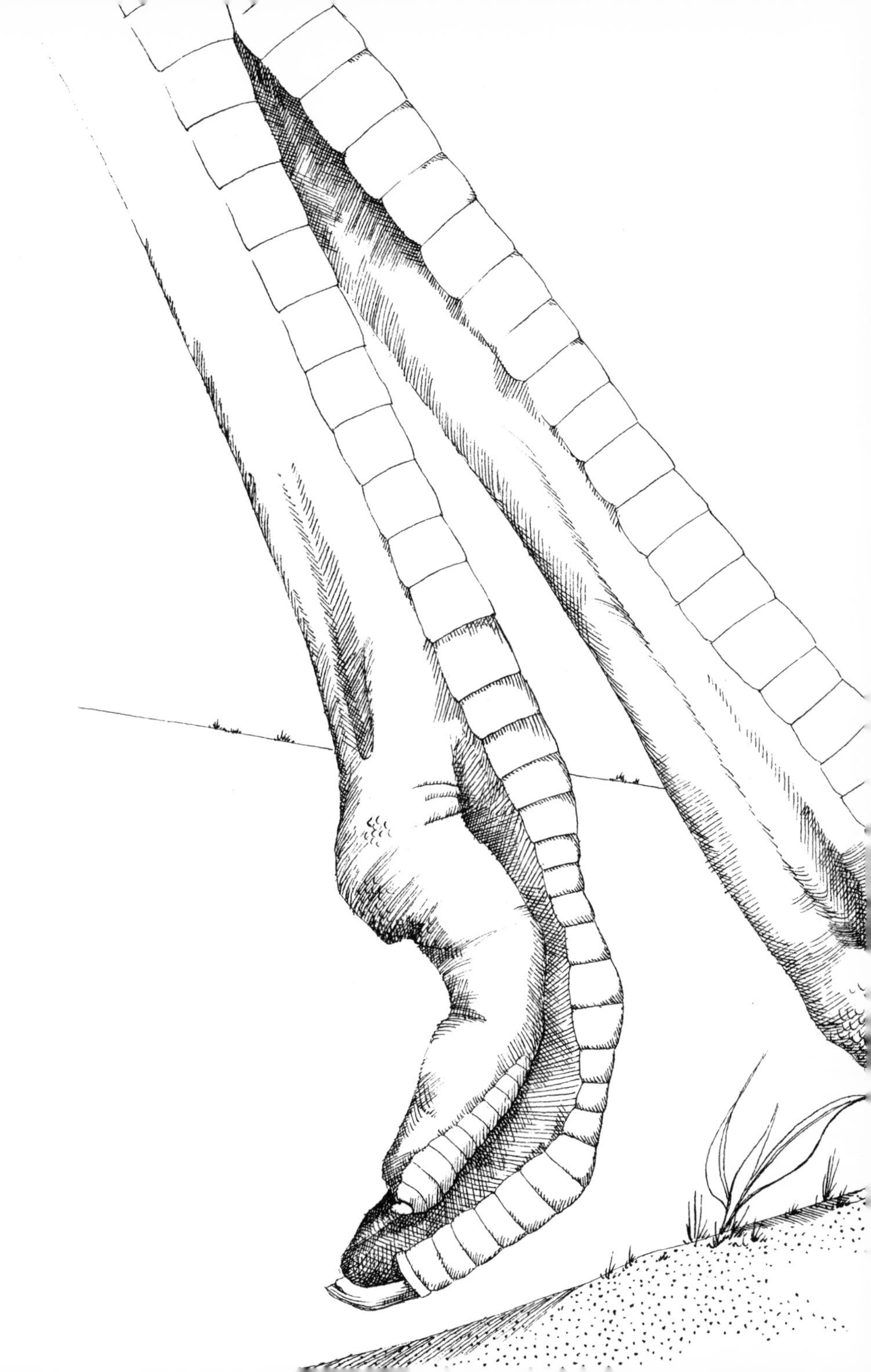

They're securest,
swiftest, surest
on their wings
above the ground.

Most birds surely
walk quite poorly.

Most birds merely
hop around.

Ostriches never
can dip and glide
or sit on the wind
to take a ride,
or look from the sky
at silver slivers
of roads and canyons
and creeks and rivers.

But OSTRICHES
never
can fly at all.
They're far too big
and their wings
too small.

Over the elms
and over the willows,

Over the pools
and ponds and billows,

Over the hills
and heights and hollows

Woodpeckers fly,
and gulls, and swallows.

Over the streams
and over the shallows,

Over the marigolds
and mallows,

Over the meadows
and the narrows

Orioles fly,
and hawks, and sparrows.

U. S. 1554632

To Avis
who can fly.
But ostriches . . .

BY THE AUTHOR:

Best Little House

But Ostriches . . .

Clean as a Whistle

Going Barefoot

I Like Weather

In One Door and Out the Other

In the Middle of the Night

Like Nothing at All

Listen, Rabbit

My Mother and I

Sing, Little Mouse

Skip Around the Year

Up, Up the Mountain

We Went Looking

Where Does Everyone Go?

COPYRIGHT © 1970 BY AILEEN FISHER

ILLUSTRATIONS COPYRIGHT © 1970 BY PETER PARNALL

ALL RIGHTS RESERVED. EXCEPT FOR USE IN A REVIEW, THE REPRODUCTION OR UTILIZATION OF THIS WORK IN ANY FORM OR BY ANY ELECTRONIC, MECHANICAL, OR OTHER MEANS NOW KNOWN OR HEREAFTER INVENTED, INCLUDING XEROGRAPHY, PHOTOCOPYING, AND RECORDING, AND IN ANY INFORMATION STORAGE AND RETRIEVAL SYSTEM IS FORBIDDEN WITHOUT THE WRITTEN PERMISSION OF THE PUBLISHER.

MANUFACTURED IN THE UNITED STATES OF AMERICA

L.C. CARD 74-106571

1 2 3 4 5 6 7 8 9 10

BUT OSTRICHES...

BY AILEEN FISHER

Illustrated by Peter Parnall

Thomas Y. Crowell Company New York

BUT
OSTRICHES...